50p

Knight Rider
Annual

© 1982 by Universal City Studios, Inc.
All Rights Reserved.

Photographs supplied by Shooting Star/Transworld and
Universal City Studios, Inc.

Published by
GRANDREAMS LTD.,
Jadwin House, 205/211 Kentish Town Road, London NW5.
Printed in Holland.

D1349762

£2.95

Flying The F.L.A.G.

The Foundation for Law And Government: *when you spell it out like that, it doesn't sound all that interesting. Call it F.L.A.G. and mention Michael Knight and his car, K.I.T.T., and you have an entirely different game, where the war against crime is carried on undercover and outside the rules. It wasn't originally intended like that, but then if the world had been the way we hoped it was, there'd be no need for F.L.A.G. in the first place.*

Unfortunately, the world isn't like that, and it was left to a man who knew all too well about having his hopes raised and then dashed to try to do something about it. That man was Wilton Knight, and his story starts way back before the Second World War.

A self-educated inventor in the near-genius class, Wilton Knight made several fortunes in the field of aeroplane and automotive design, his first million coming before the age of 22. But, each in turn, those fortunes vanished, stolen away for the most part by ruthless and unscrupulous business enemies, who bent or broke the laws, and still somehow managed to get away with it. It was events like these that started to shape Wilton Knight's thinking:

in an ordinary situation, a run-of-the-mill criminal would confront the law directly, by robbery or murder, and at the point the police would move in to clean up the "break in the rules", and usually win out. But when the criminal side-stepped the law, cheating his way into areas outside the rules and possibly even corrupting the guardians of order, then injustice was being done that needed to be fought on another level.

With his last fortune . . . the one that his enemies didn't get away with . . . Wilton Knight decided to set up the Foundation for Law and Government, realising that in doing so he could not only help to solve his own problems, but also those of others similarly entangled with crooks operating outside the law. That was in 1965, and Knight ran the Foundation until his death, from cancer, in 1982.

F.L.A.G.'s headquarters are in southern California, near Los Angeles, though it also has offices in New York, Washington, Chicago and elsewhere. Much of the Foundation's work is restricted to purely legal affairs, fighting its battles in the courts, and it was pretty much for this purpose that Wilton Knight brought in an old

friend of his from his war days, Deven Miles, as chairman of the organisation. Together, he and Miles picked the lawyers for F.L.A.G.'s legal branch; and it was the Englishman Miles who took over the Foundation after Knight's death.

The son of a British Member of Parliament, Miles first met Knight while they were each doing undercover work in the Second World War. His parents having been killed in the bombing of London, Miles eventually emigrated to the United States in the early 1950s, became a citizen, and started working for the government. It's from this work that he's managed to keep up his wealth of connections, with everyone from the C.I.A. to the most obscure department of the government, and that vast knowledge and experience made him the perfect man to head all of F.L.A.G.'s branches, be they legal, administrative, scientific or whatever.

Shortly before his death, Wilton Knight and Miles realised that even the Foundation itself was not without its faults, for it too tried to play by the rules as much as possible, while its opponents continued to ignore them as usual. A change of game plan was needed, and in the late 1970s,

F.L.A.G. began to move toward a new concept which would enable it to fight crime much more on its own level. The first part of that concept was the production of a virtually indestructible car, the Knight Industries Two Thousand, or K.I.T.T., with its computerised robot brain and arsenal of exotic gadgetry. The second part of the plan was to find a driver for it.

Michael Arthur Long was that man, born 1949 in Reno, Nevada; "killed" in the same town in 1982. At 20, he had joined the Green Berets and done counter-intelligence work in Vietnam. Fighting his way out of a prisoner of war camp, he received head-injuries which later required a metal plate to be inserted in his skull. After the war he returned to Reno and the police department, rising to the rank of detective lieutenant. Then, one night

on a case, he was shot in the head by an informant and left for dead.

But thanks to the metal plate, and the efforts begun by Wilton Knight, who found him lying on the highway, Michael Long did not die. Not entirely, anyway. His face was rebuilt by plastic surgery, and he was given a new name and identity; that of Michael Knight. Underneath all this still lurks the same drive for justice that Long used to have, the drive that made Wilton Knight pick him in the first place; but Michael Knight now is a man without a history, a man who comes upon the scene and departs again without anyone knowing why or where he's come from.

Few indeed know his identity: Wilton Knight is dead, and both Deven Miles and K.I.T.T. have good reasons of their own for keeping quiet. And the

only other person involved is April Curtis, the beautiful brainy blonde computer genius and electronics wiz, recently brought in by the Foundation to keep K.I.T.T. abreast of the very latest developments in programming and development.

Together, they make a team: Deven Miles, the aristocratic administrator with all the contacts; April Curtis, covering the scientific and technical aspects of a case; Michael Knight, the field operative, using all his very human talents to gain information and sort out the case, and not afraid to rough it with the bad guys if the occasion demands it.

And of course there's a certain very special car called K.I.T.T. A car that thinks, talks and moves by itself.

Together they make a very small part of the Foundation for Law and Government, though an important one . . . but, also . . . together they make a very large part of . . . KNIGHT RIDER.

Games People Play

Michael Knight shivered and pulled his car-coat closer round himself as he slammed Kitt's door and turned to follow Deven Miles across the street. He didn't usually come as far north as Greenton in the winter and it was on days like this that one thing he appreciated most amongst Kitt's gadgetry was the heating system. The sidewalks were piled with dirty snow, and the sky was heavy with leaden grey clouds. His breath curling steamily before his face, Michael hurried after Deven, joining him just as he reached the doorway of the Black Domino Restaurant.

"I still don't see why we didn't bring April with us," said Michael as they paused to let a group of fur-coated diners out of the door. "I would have thought she and this Kelly woman would have got on like a house on fire."

"Precisely why she's not with us," Deven told him as the doorway cleared. "It seems that Doctor Kelly's employers at the Adcom Corporation are so paranoid about her work they insisted that no computer or electronics people be allowed near her...even ours!"

"Heavy…" shrugged Michael as they entered the restaurant, pausing as a waiter came toward them.

"She is a genius," Deven reminded Michael, then turned to tell the waiter they were expected.

"Yeah, and I'll bet she looks just like a sweet little old granny, too," said Michael, as the waiter led them toward the table where a group from Adcom sat idly looking at menus.

"Hardly," said Deven softly, gesturing ahead. There were three people sat at the restaurant table. One was a muscular man of about thirty with close-cropped hair and a flat, boxer's nose. The second was the executive type, about fifty, wearing an immaculate suit and thick-rimmed glasses, grey-haired and worried-looking. The third was a stunning long-haired blonde, casually dressed in a chunky blue jumper and black jeans.

Maybe Doctor Kelly hadn't turned up yet, thought Michael, but there were only two other places set at the table; presumably for Deven and himself.

"Mr Riddington, Chief Executive of Adcom," Deven began, gesturing toward the older man. "This is Michael Knight…"

"Call me Joe," said Riddington, adjusting his glasses before turning to the girl at his side. "This is Doctor Lesley Kelly!"

"How do you do," said the blonde dryly, giving Michael only the briefest of glances before returning her attention to the menu. He opened his mouth, about to say something, then shut it again and shrugged.

"And this is Pike," said Riddington hurriedly, pointing a slightly sweating hand toward the other man. "From our security division."

"Pleased to meet you all," nodded Michael, as he and Deven took their seats at the table. And after a few more pleasantries, the conversation turned to the reason for their meeting.

"Your job basically will be to protect Doctor Kelly," Riddington told Michael. "It's to do with a project she's working on for Adcom, which is due to be completed in four days time."

"And what exactly are you working on?" Michael asked, addressing the blonde directly.

"I'd really rather not say," Lesley Kelly replied, then shrugged as she realised she'd have to give a little more of an explanation than that. "It's to do with computer games. You remember how Space Invaders revolutionised the whole games' industry? Sure there've been developments since then, but most of the video-cartridges you get these days trace their origins back to 'Invaders'. What I'm working on is a new piece of microprocessor technology that'll just blow that stuff away. It'll be as important a new breakthrough as Space Invaders was in its time."

"And I think that's about as much as we ought to say at the moment," put in Riddington hurriedly, glancing around nervously. "As you can imagine, something like that is worth a fortune to Adcom; but it'd also be worth a fortune to our competitors. In the last six months there've been three attempts at industrial espionage centring on Doctor Kelly's laboratory."

"But they haven't got anywhere," said Lesley. "I don't know what you're so worried about."

"What I'm worried about is that until we get a working model built in four days time, and see if the thing actually works under test conditions, we can't apply for a patent. Until it's patented, we're not safe. Until it's built, it's not patented. And unless we manage to keep you here in Greenton for the next four days, it's not going to get built."

"I told you, you worry too much," Lesley put in, glancing up as her steak arrived on the table. "I can look after myself alright."

"Look, you seem to be talking round all this in circles," said Michael. "Will somebody please put me in the picture as to exactly what I'm here for?"

Riddington shrugged wearily, then raised a half-smile. "There are millions of dollars at stake here, perhaps billions. And our competitors, especially the foreign ones, would give their eye-teeth for a piece of the action. When we had those espionage attempts, we destroyed most of the working notes. All the vital stuff is carried around in Doctor Kelly's head, until we get that patent application ready. And three days ago, some guys tried to kidnap her."

"It was clumsy," sneered Lesley.

"Even Pike managed to beat them off."

"We informed the police," Riddington continued, ignoring Pike's grimace of disdain. "But our stuff's hardly a state secret or of military significance. And they're too stretched for manpower to give us any help until a crime's actually been committed. That's why we turned to the Foundation. Your job, Michael, will be to stay with Doctor Kelly every minute for the next four days. There's a spare room at her house where you can put up."

Michael could think of worse prospects as he glanced toward the beautiful computer expert, but her response was less than enthusiastic. "I told you I can look after myself," she snapped at her boss. "All this nonsense about me being kidnapped by our competitors and smuggled off to the Far East to have my brain drained of secrets with truth drugs."

"It's been known to happen, Miss Kelly," Michael told her. "And if there's been one kidnap attempt already..."

"Precisely," put in Deven. "And that's why the Foundation's prepared to take an interest. I'm sure you won't find Michael too unpleasant to keep company with for a few days."

Realising she had no choice, Lesley finally shrugged and got on with her meal. The rest of the conversation was unimportant; and then Riddington paid the bill and Deven prepared to return to base. Lesley Kelly was duly handed over to Michael for protection, and as they walked out of the restaurant he started toward Kitt.

"I have my *own* car," Lesley announced.

"Sure...but you'll like mine better." Michael told her, opening the passenger door and ushering her inside. "We can pick yours up later."

By the time Michael took his seat beside her, he could see her studying the dashboard intently, her eyes running over the computer console, the monitor screens, the auto-pilot, and so on. But she said nothing until he glanced toward her as he turned the ignition.

"Not bad," she finally admitted, then turned to look away from him out of the window with a bored air. "I suppose you'd better take me to my lab for the rest of the afternoon."

The remainder of the day passed in dull routine. Michael stuck with Lesley all the time she was at the Adcom building, but what she was doing was quite beyond him. Driving her home, she grudgingly cooked him a meal from the freezer, spent nearly an hour talking to her boy-friend on the phone, and then pointedly ignored him and watched the television for the rest of the evening. The next day wasn't much better, and he took a cheap horror-novel with him to pass the time.

"You want to go out and relax this evening?" Michael asked as Kitt returned them to her house on the edge of town.

"Okay, sure," Michael agreed, reaching into his pocket. As she produced a lipstick from her handbag, he inserted the device into the end of the holder and gave it back to her. Then, when she was in the bath, he went through her handbag again; this time inserting a tiny homing device *and* microphone into her purse. It wasn't exactly honest, but Lesley Kelly didn't

"I have a date with Roger," she told him shortly, reaching for the door-handle, but finding it impossible to open.

"Not yet," Michael told her, switching Kitt to Surveillance Mode. "Let me check out the area first."

The scanners showed no sign of movement and no extraordinary heat sources within a hundred yards, and it seemed as if the house was waiting empty for them. Even Lesley seemed impressed by Kitt's technology this time, but she said nothing.

"You can open the door now," Michael told her, and soon he was following her into the house.

"What time do we go out?" he asked, settling himself into a chair in the living room.

"I go out at eight," she told him. "You do what you like!"

Michael smiled.

"I'm going out for a private dinner with my boyfriend!" snapped Lesley, suddenly losing her temper. "I do *not* want you tagging along and making it a threesome! Besides, I'm going in Roger's car...and it's only got two seats!"

"Okay," agreed Michael. "I'll try to make sure you don't see me all evening. But if I decide to go out to dinner and turn up at the same restaurant...oh, and you'll be carrying a homing device round with you as well..."

Lesley stared at him speechlessly for a moment, then made some show of giving in. "A homing device, maybe," she agreed, picking up her handbag. "But no microphones!"

seem to *want* to be helped for some reason, and Michael had his job to do.

Roger Pyle, a fair-haired well-dressed man in his mid-thirties, arrived precisely at eight o'clock, nodding curtly toward Michael before whisking Lesley outside to his waiting coupé. Michael waited until they were clear of the drive and out of sight, then ran out and jumped into Kitt.

The Knight 2000's monitors were soon picking up the signals from the homing devices, though Michael decided to be discreet and not listen in to the bug. Putting Kitt into Pursuit Mode, he settled back and started running through the car's computer records as they drove. But Roger Pyle seemed to have a completely clear past. There was nothing on him at all.

Keeping well behind and out of sight, Michael followed the couple into Greenton once more, and was hardly surprised to find them turning up at the Black Domino restaurant again. It did seem to be the only decent restaurant in town.

Checking where Pyle had left his car in the park, Michael slipped into the restaurant by the side entrance and found himself an alcove in the corner which gave him a good view of the main dining area. Lesley was easy to spot, blonde-haired and black-dressed, a serious expression on her face as she talked with Roger. They didn't exactly look like a young couple out enjoying themselves, but there was no way Michael could hear their conversation from that distance. A waitress appeared and he ordered Chile con Carne, then settled down to wait.

Soon after his order arrived, Lesley looked up, glanced round the room, paused as she saw him, and then turned to whisper to Roger. A few minutes later she got up, carrying her handbag, and headed across the restaurant toward the Ladies Room, passing Michael without a word.

Fifteen minutes passed without any sign of her reappearing, then twenty. Michael summoned the nearest waitress.

"Do me a favour?" he asked, flashing her his most winning smile. "A friend of mine…blonde hair, black dress…went into the Ladies a while back, and she hasn't come out. You think you could go in there and check whether she's okay?"

The waitress hesitated a moment, then nodded. As she disappeared, Michael glanced round toward Roger Pyle, saw him still sitting there, then turned his attention back to the door.

The waitress reappeared a few moments later, clutching an open handbag. Michael got up hurriedly and went to join her.

"No one in there, Mister," the waitress explained. "But the Fire Exit's been opened, and I found this bag dropped on the floor. The stuff was scattered all over the place."

"Blast!" muttered Michael under his breath, checking the contents of the bag. The lipstick was still there, but there was no sign of the purse. Puzzled, he turned to look back toward the restaurant…only to see that Roger Pyle had disappeared too.

Pulling a ten-dollar bill from his pocket to pay for the meal, Michael grabbed the handbag from the waitress and dashed out into the car-park. There was no sign of the coupé now, and Michael dashed toward Kitt.

Something about all this didn't add up. Why was Lesley so dismissive about her own safety? Why had her "boyfriend" disappeared at the same time as she did? And if she'd been kidnapped by outsiders, why had she been allowed to take her purse with her, but not her handbag? Putting Kitt on Pursuit Mode once more, Michael set off after them, following the extra homing device; and this time, he decided, he'd listen on the microphone as well...

"...Thought we'd never get away from him..." he heard Lesley say. "Damn Riddington and his last minute security ideas!"

"Yeah, but we're away from him *now*," came Roger Pyle's voice. "Another half an hour and we'll be at the airport...and then you'll be safely on your way to the guys at the Toshiro Company..."

"...And a contract worth ten million in the first year alone!" Lesley concluded. Michael didn't need to hear any more. A quick check of Kitt's records showed that the Toshiro company was Adcom's biggest competitor in the computer-games world, and now it all fell into place. The whole thing was a set-up.

Lesley Kelly wasn't being kidnapped. She was running out with her new invention, "stealing" if from Adcom and disappearing. To turn up later in Japan no doubt with a new name and new looks to sell the product to the opposition. The previous kidnap attempt, and the industrial espionage, were just red herrings...designed to make the story of her "kidnap" more believable.

It started to snow fairly heavily as Michael made his way out of town. Not that that would be any particular worry to Kitt with its superb road-holding, but Michael decided to pile on more speed and get things wrapped up as fast as possible. Cutting all the lights except the side-lamps, he roared down the highway in pursuit.

"Let me check that I've still got my plane ticket," Lesley's voice announced as Michael finally got the coupé in sight. "It's here in my purse somewhere."

A few moments later, there was a burst of static, and then silence. Lesley had obviously found the bug, and from the fact that the coupé suddenly speeded up, Michael guessed they'd spotted him. The snow began to fall more thickly, but Kitt was now close enough to keep up the pursuit without the aid of direct sight or homing devices.

The chase continued for another five minutes along open country roads, the speedo showing a three figure number in spite of the weather conditions. Michael brought Kitt up to about ten yards behind the coupé and held it there.

Roger Pyle glanced back at him, then turned his attention back to the road; but not in time to judge an up-coming curve. Michael was already hitting the brakes as the coupé left the road, bumped across some snow-covered grass, and plunged into an ice-covered lake.

As the coupé sank out of sight into the dark waters and the broken slabs of ice began to float back over it, Michael knew there was no time for hesitation. "Seal up, Kitt!" he yelled, turning on the interior oxygen and taking his foot off the brake. "And turn all your spot-lights on!"

"You can't be serious, Michael!" protested Kitt, but Michael kept the car running straight across the snow-covered grass, and then plunged through the ice-floe a few feet away from where the coupé had gone in.

The water in the lake was black as pitch, but only about six feet deep, and as soon as Michael felt the car hit the bottom he gunned the accelerator and wrenched over the wheel. There was no way of knowing what lay on the bottom of the lake, but he managed to turn the car round in front of the sunken coupé, and after a couple of seconds his spot-lights found it.

Fortunately the coupé had landed right side up, and with the windows tightly wound up against the cold, there was still a pocket of air trapped inside under the roof. But water was seeping in round the edges of the door, already up to their waists, and Michael could see Lesley thrashing around in panic as it rose steadily higher.

Michael headed Kitt straight toward the coupé, the impact as their bumpers collided bending the bodywork and allowing the water to seep in yet more quickly.

"Push, Kitt!" yelled Michael

desperately as he saw the water rising round Lesley's shoulders. The Knight 2000's wheels span uselessly in the soft sand for a moment, then found some grip. The coupé started to move slowly backward up the lake shore, but it was so heavy with water that progress uphill was desperately slow — Lesley and Roger were standing up in their seats now, heads pressed to roof, as the water lapped round their chins.

Then at last the coupé broke the surface, and with a final surge Kitt managed to push it out onto the bank, following along behind. Water was spraying out round the coupé's doors as Michael jumped out of Kitt and ran forward.

Water gushed everywhere as he wrenched open the coupé door and pulled Pyle out into the cold night air, bunching his free hand into a fist. But there was no further resistance now. After a quick check that his captives were physically okay, he loaded them into the back of Kitt and prepared to head back toward Greenton. Joe Riddington would be in for an awful shock when he got them back to Adcom.

There was a sound of teeth chattering and shivering from the back, and Michael just knew Kitt was going to give him a hard time later about the lake-water on the upholstery. But for now he just turned the heating system up full and got on with the driving. He sure did appreciate that little gadget.

A Knight And His Damsel

Bad news for all those female fans of the *Knight Rider* series: star David Hasselhoff is planning to marry. The good news is that he reckons that his fiancée, 30-year old actress Catherine Hickland, has just about saved his life, for the last few years, despite his seeming success, have not been without their problems.

The worst of those problems centred on the death of another important woman in his life, Joyce Selznick, his close friend and manager. She was the one who first set him on the road to stardom, and she was the one who, like a mother, kept him in line during his days in Hollywood. But the David Hasselhoff story goes back much further than that, of course.

"I decided while I was still in junior school in Baltimore that I wanted to be an actor," he says. "I've never thought of doing anything else."

But there were others with their eyes on the tall student, now grown up to be a handsome 6ft 4in 29-year old. "I became a prime target for every coach. Then they discovered I wasn't co-ordinated enough for basketball or football, so they left me alone to get on with my acting."

From there he enrolled at the Academy of Dramatic Arts in Rochester, Michigan, and then went on to the California Institute of the Arts near Los Angeles. "I spent two wonderful years there learning my craft, but I decided I should go 'out there'. So, with a little luck I landed a part in the Los

Angeles Free Shakespeare Festival's production of *As You Like It*. Unfortunately, the job did have one big drawback. 'Free' was the operative word. I had to become a part-time waiter to keep from starving.''

It was while he was serving tables at the Marina City Club that Joyce Selznick spotted him, and she got him roles in shows like *Police Story, Griffin and Phoenix*, and a number of commercials. Then his big break came with the role of Dr. Snapper Foster in a show called *The Young and the Restless*, which kept him employed for over six years. Over-employed, in fact, for he was averaging about three hours sleep a night and working virtually every day. It was toward the end of that period that Joyce Selznick died, and David started to go to pieces.

"It's hard to believe, but it's all true," he says. "I was a wild, crazy man before I met Catherine. I was drinking too much and staying out all night because I couldn't face my lonely home life. But our love has turned my whole life around. Before I met her I'd go out on the town and sometimes I'd wake up in the night and not have a clue where I was. God knows what would have happened if I hadn't met Cathy . . . I'd probably be in the ground by now.

"And then I met Cathy at a party in New York. We got on great but nothing serious happened until she moved to the West Coast three months afterwards. Now in the year or so we've been together everything has changed.

The biggest thrill in my life is coming home to her.''

Cathy plays a character called Courtney Marshall in an American soap-opera called *Texas*, and wants to keep working after their marriage. But when that might be still isn't quite certain. David still has a few woman problems; this time with his adoring female fans, some of whom just can't restrain themselves:

''Cathy gets mad when they approach me in the street and I can't blame her. These women tell me they think I'm gorgeous or something like that and invite me home . . . right in front of her. I tell them that Cathy is my fiancée but it doesn't put them off.

''Sometimes Cathy's so angry she's ready to tear their hair out. It really upsets her but there's nothing I can do about it. I can't stop them recognising me if I'm in a hit show.''

The 'hit show' is *Knight Rider*, of course, and since that chance meeting at a New York party, David's life has really taken something of an upswing. ''Since we met I have landed a starring role in a hit TV series and I am in love with the most beautiful woman in the world. Who could ask for more than that?

''We are planning to get married, but we won't rush into having children. Time is so tight with the show that I don't have enough time to devote to Cathy, let alone any children.

''But we are planning to buy a home where we can just let the phone ring off the hook and ignore it

while we enjoy each other."

And rather than going out on the town, David has now found other ways to let off steam . . . one of which is doing some of his own stunts on *Knight Rider*. "I hung from a helicopter the other day," he says, smiling, "and Cathy refused to come on the set to watch. And they let me do some highspeed driving, which I really enjoy.

"But I care too much about Cathy to do anything stupid. I spent enough of my life, before she came along, risking my health."

And there are other ways of filling in spare time, too, like serving tables at a restaurant in Atlanta, Georgia. Just like the bad old days? Not really. "I enjoy it," he says, "because I own the place!"

Rebecca Holden
– The Beauty With Brains

April Curtis is the 'new' girl in the prestigious Foundation for Law and Government taking over from Bonnie Barstow as the computer expert and KITT's programmer at the start of the second series. It took the producers a long time to find the right actress to play April but they eventually got a real winner in Rebecca. Although a relative newcomer to T.V. she was an instant hit with the millions of Knight Rider fans all round the world. During a break in the hectic filming schedule, Rebecca took time out to talk to us about her past, her present and her future.

WHAT IS YOUR BACKGROUND?

I was born in Austin, Texas and I moved to Dallas. I studied the piano from the time I was 5 years old. I think I've always been on the stage performing in on capacity or another. I was in the choir and all the school plays and all the musicals. When I was in High School, I performed in the well-known attraction, *'Six Flags Over Texas'*, the big amusement park. I studied voice all the time through High School. I had planned to be an opera singer. I studied classical singing since I was about 13 years old along with classical piano, all the way through college.

I went to college at North Texas State University where I had a major in voice and a minor in piano. Even though I was in all the musical plays we did, I never thought I would be an actress. I thought I would be a musician or a singer. I never thought about going into T.V. or movies.

Along with my studies of classical music, I have a love of country music. I guess being born in Texas, it's just something that's in you, the love of country music. Now, I sing a lot of 'pop' music, and I'm now getting ready to do a

record.

I finished college early because I went to summer school and took many classes each year. After I graduated from college, I went to New York to study singing and I wanted a record deal too.

HOW DID YOUR BREAK INTO SHOW BUSINESS HAPPEN?

One day I was with a friend of mine who was a past Miss America and she was like a big sister to me.

She had already been in New York for a long time and she had gotten many rejections from commercial auditions and she was tired and decided to go home. We went to lunch together to sort of say 'good-bye' and she had to go to her agency to pick up some pictures and things. The head of the agency came out and said to me, 'Would you go out on an audition for me for a shampoo commercial?' I told him that I wasn't a model, I was a singer, but I said, 'yes' and went on the audition.

I was blessed with pretty thick hair and I got the job. I thought it was kind of neat, so I did the commercials for Breck Shampoo. I was the 'Breck Girl' and I worked for them for about 3 years.

I continued studying my music all that time and I'm still studying. I was taking private music lessons. From that point on I started doing a lot of commercials. Most of the commercials were for beauty products. I was the Princess on the white horse for British Sterling.

The funniest and the hardest commercial I ever did was for a bread company. I was a Mermaid and I wore a gorgeous costume of beads that looked like shimmering scales. My feet of course were tied together in the tail and the costume had a top to it. The costume was really designed for me to wear sitting on the bank of the water but when we got on the set the director told me that I was going to be in the water swimming. The costume with all the beads was very heavy and I went straight to the bottom of the water.

I had to swim and it's good that I'm a very strong swimmer, because they wanted to see the tail above the water. It was 7 in the morning and freezing cold. Even though I turned blue, it was all in the line of duty.

Then I sang on a Cerebral Palsy Telethon and the head of a big theatrical agency in New York asked me to go with them, also as a singer. I did a night club act and toured all over the Caribbean. The agency thought I needed to be in California. When we told Bobby, my husband, he said, 'If that's where you need to be, that's where we'll be.' So, we came out here. Bobby's oil business was to the point where he didn't need to be in Texas all the time.

I was in High School and Bobby was finishing college when we first met. He always laughed about, 'Robbing the Cradle'. At that time it seemed like more of an age difference. We were just friends then, buddies, and finally it developed into more. I think that's nice for a relationship to begin that way because you know each other real well as friends. We were both living in Dallas then.

Bobby had studied business and real estate in college but when he graduated from college he just decided to start his own oil company. Usually the oil business is very closed and you can get into it only if your family is in it. But Bobby hired wonderful experts to work with him. He gets the land leases and then he goes in and he drills for oil. He has offices in Texas and we keep an apartment in New York and our home in Los Angeles. We're in L.A. most of the time because this is where I need to be. I feel so lucky that I have a husband who can say to me that he has his dreams and his goals and that I helped him to accomplish his dreams and now he wants to help me accomplish mine. He feels that he can operate his business wherever he has a telephone so if L.A. is where I need to be, this is where we'll be.

Most men have a 9-5 job where they need to be and they can't move around so we're lucky that Bobby can carry his office with him as long as he has a telephone. Bobby grew up in a very large Italian household where 'woman's place was in the home'. At first he thought that when I went off to New York I would get it out of my system, then I would come back home and we would get married and be a home maker and do charity work, play bridge and have 10 kids. Fortunately Bobby loved and cared enough about me that he said, 'You deserve to have your dreams too.' His family is very proud of me. They love to see things about me in the newspapers and they always watch all my shows.

We do look forward to the time when we will have children. If it were up to Bobby we would have had 6 kids by now. We can't go into a store and pass a little baby without his saying, 'When are you going to give me one?' But, Bobby knows that this isn't the time right now and that we'll have plenty of time to start a family. So, things have a way, I think, of working out. I think that you always know when the time is right to do things.

When I came to L.A. I did a lot of guest appearances on shows like: 'Taxi', 'Magnum P.I.', 'Three's Company', 'Quincy', 'Love Boat'; I did guest stars on practically every prime time show on T.V.

I was offered some pilots which I turned down. I was offered a contract deal with N.B.C., a contract deal with A.B.C., and a contract deal with Aaron Spelling. I got very nervous because my agent kept turning down all those offers. I told my agent that people would stop calling if we turned down everything. He told me to believe him and trust him that it was the right thing to do. He didn't want to take a contract deal where we didn't know what the specific project would be that I would be put into, that isn't wise. Fortunately I wasn't in a position where I HAD to work at that time. If I really needed the money and had to have a contract deal to have a salary coming in, that's one thing, but I was in a position where I could hold out, so I waited until I could take the right thing. My agent didn't really want me to do any T.V., he wanted me to do only film.

In fact I did do a film, a Japanese film called, *'The Last Hero'*. It became the biggest box office hit in the Far East for 1982.

Then, N.B.C. came to us and asked if I would consider doing *'Knight Rider'* and said that they were creating a new character and that the show was picked up for 22 more episodes. I told my agent that I thought it was a great show. We have a very good new time slot in the Fall. The show has developed such a following. It has a T.V.Q. in the top 10, it's number 6. It's above *'Magnum P.I.'* and *'60 Minutes'*. It's very rare that you can walk into a show that's already a hit like that. Usually you have to go through making the pilot, waiting to see if it sells. Then they keep you on hold for like 2 seasons, so I'm very lucky. In a sense my agent was right holding out.

TELL ME ABOUT YOUR DOG

It's a West Highland White Terrier. His name is Champion Happy Macs Superstar. Happy Macs is the Kennel name. We call him 'Soupy' for short from Superstar. I showed him myself to his Championship. My parents raise show dogs. From the time that I was a little kid that was our family hobby. I raised him since he was a puppy.

ABOUT WORKING ON 'KNIGHT RIDER'

This is my first season on the show and we've shot 22 episodes. We're on a 7-day schedule. It was very easy for me to join the show because the people involved in the show from actors to the crew are the nicest, nicest people in the world.

I work a lot with both David Hasselhoff and Edward Mulhare. They have been wonderful to me and so have the producers. I feel so lucky because the producers sat down with me and told me they really wanted to expand the character I'm playing. They said, 'We know a show can't survive over a year on gimmicks or stunts or cars or tricks. You have to have human relationships and people that the audience cares enough about to tune in and watch the show.' So, the producers wanted to develop a relationship between David and me and between Edward and me. They are even hinting at a little romance between David's character and mine but I don't know if they'll do it or how far that part of our relationship will go. We'll see.

The producers are saying now that they want my character to go undercover with David and not just be in the semi-truck fixing the car. They want me actually out with David. They told me that they know I'm a singer and they want to use that and maybe have me go undercover as a singer.

They know that I do many different things and they also told me they want to utilize all my talents by bringing them in and use them as story ideas. They really want to get to know me and what I can do so they can employ as much of my abilities in the scripts. That attitude is so nice. To get producers who want to work with you and want your ideas and input and utilize the things you have to offer, is so nice. I feel blessed.

I love my character because she's so intelligent as well as attractive. That's what's so nice about her. I've appeared in a lot of 'sitcoms' as a kind of ditzy, ding-bat lady and even though I like to play those characters because they're fun, I don't ever want to be stereotyped as someone who only plays those kinds of roles, those kind of parts. If you get into shows where 'ditzy' ladies are all that people see you as, then it really is difficult to make the transition to playing more intelligent and meaty parts and characters with serious abilities and depth. So, even though it was fun to play comedy and more cartoonish characters, I'm really thrilled with my character on *'Knight Rider'*. She's a computer expert,

an electronics wiz. She programmes the car KITT. She does experiments on him constantly, inventing new feats for him (KITT, the car) to accomplish. She's a real brainy girl. It's nice that you've got this lady who has definitely got a brain and she still cares about her appearance and is still feminine and likes to dress in pretty clothes and yet at the same time, she's in a man's job, but she doesn't want to be a man. I really like her a lot and how nice it is to go to work and work on a character that you enjoy.

How nice it is and how lucky to be able to get up in the morning and go to a job you love especially when you think of all those people who hate getting up and going to work in the morning. I hope to be with the show until the very end, whenever that'll be.

I got an offer for a film on my first break in January 1984, so I'll also be doing other things too. It's a good feeling to have other things to do in case something happens to the show but I have a feeling 'Knight Rider' will be around for a long time. So many people say when they learn that I'm on the show, that it's their kid's favourite show.

It's the gimmick of the car KITT and all the computers that hooked the kids in the first place and intrigued them about the show but you've got to have people in there too, relationships.

Besides being a 'gorgeous hunk', David is so wonderful and easy to work with. He is a nice, nice guy and a lot of fun.

I've worked on so many 'Prime Time' shows that I've seen a lot of working environments and this 'Knight Rider' is such a pleasure to work on. Everyone working on the show is such a family, they're so united and everyone is so much fun as people and they enjoy their work so much that I have a ball. I hate the days when I don't have to go into work. It's that wonderful spirit that comes from the top and it is felt all the way through everyone working on the show.

"Driving all the way to Venezuela, senor? A long way." The frontier guard flicked through Michael Knight's passport briefly, and then handed it back to him. Michael smiled and nodded politely, though his story was far from true. His business would take him no further than right here in the Central American republic of Havamala, though there was no point in telling the guard that. He'd probably have to be a lot less polite when he was coming out of the country as well, but he'd worry about that when he came to it.

"Take Highway Five," the guard told him, turning and gesturing down the road. "At the next fork, turn right. That'll keep you out of trouble . . . and you wouldn't want your nice shiny new car messed up, would you?"

"I certainly wouldn't," smiled Michael as the guard waved him through the barrier. Hitting the accelerator, he headed on into the hills, leaving the frontier post behind and looking for the fork. It was only two minutes away, and as soon as he found it he pulled the wheel hard over toward the left. Toward Highway Four.

"I'm still not sure this is a wise idea, Michael," Kitt told him as the speed built up.

"Neither am I, Kitt," Michael agreed. "But we've taken the job, so I guess we're just going to have to go through with it. Even if it does mean driving through the middle of a war."

The war wasn't Michael's major concern, however; in fact, Deven had told him specifically that he wasn't to get involved with one side or the other. The guerrillas probably had more people on their side, but the government forces were better armed. It was about evenly matched, and both sides were claiming to be in the right. Not the sort of situation for a lone American citizen to want to get involved in.

But that was the trouble. One American citizen was involved; right up to her pretty young neck. Melanie Black, known locally as the "Bandit Queen". And she was the one Michael Knight was coming to collect.

Looking ahead, Michael could see the smoke of exploding shells rising from the hills a few miles away. He decided to put Kitt on automatic pilot and review his mission one more time before the action started.

Melanie Black's photograph and record were soon displayed on the monitor screens, and Michael tried to memorise her features for later. She was dark haired, in her mid-twenties, and fairly pretty. Unfortunately, she was also extremely deadly. Suspected of four armed robberies, two murders and sundry acts of urban terrorism . . . and that was only back in the States, before she skipped the country.

Then, about a year ago, she'd come to Havamala, soon after the guerrilla war had started. It wasn't long before she'd managed to organise a group of thieves and killers, and now they were taking advantage of the situation to plunder everything they could lay their hands on. She was claiming to work for the guerrillas, but they'd long ago disowned her; for every cent she stole was shipped straight out of the country to a safe haven in the Caribbean.

In fact, nobody liked Melanie Black. Neither the Havamalan government nor the guerrillas . . . and certainly not the U.S. authorities. They wanted her back for her previous crimes, but it was impossible to extradite her. And the situation Havamala was in, it was impossible even to arrest her.

That was where Michael came in. Deven had made it sound quite simple. "Drive down to Havamala, sneak through the middle of a war-zone, get past some fairly anti-American guerrillas, pull a dangerous criminal out from the midst of her own private army, and get her back to the United States . . ." They'd see . . .

"Michael!" said Kitt suddenly, drawing his attention back to the road. "Half a mile ahead. There's a road block; a barrier, two armoured personnel carriers and about ten men."

"Government troops," remarked Michael, looking ahead. "Well, we aren't going to be able to explain what we're doing here, so government or guerrillas, we're just going to have to treat them the same. Get ready for some action, Kitt!"

The troops had spotted the approaching black car by then, waving their hands as they realised it wasn't slowing down. In fact it was getting faster and about fifty yards before the road-block, Michael hit the turbo-boost.

Moments later, the car was hurtling through the air above the barrier, while the soldiers scattered and threw themselves hurriedly to the ground.

Kitt hit the road again with a slight bump, then roared away. There was a rattle of sub-machine gun fire from behind, and one or two bullets spanged off Kitt's armoured rear, but within seconds they were clear. And the speed that Michael was driving, he thought it most unlikely they'd make any attempt to pursue.

On the other hand, they probably thought they didn't have to; for the air was suddenly full of the whistle of falling shells, and with a series of dull thuds,

they began exploding all over the hills. Hunching down in his seat, Michael kept driving as fast as the road-conditions would allow.

"I realise I'm only a machine, Michael," remarked Kitt dryly as an artillery shell burst about twenty yards away, peppering them with shrapnel, "but I *do* have this inbuilt sense of self-preservation."

"What are you trying to tell me, Kitt?" asked Michael, wrenching over the wheel to avoid a large shell-hole which cut across half the road.

"I'm telling . . . would you *please* get me out of here!"

"Yeah, I thought you were," said Michael, as bullets rattled against the bonnet, this time coming from the guerrillas.

The next half hour was unpleasant, to put it mildly. There were continual artillery barrages, rocket attacks and gunfire. There were bodies, wounded guerrillas and ruined villages. It reminded Michael far too much of Vietnam for comfort, and he was more than pleased when Kitt finally moved out of artillery range, leaving the shellfire to give a ghastly decoration to what had once been pleasant green hills. And this sort of thing had been going on all over Havamala for months.

Driving got a little easier then. There were still signs of heavy war damage for the next twenty miles, but eventually Michael began to see some of the civilian population still living in the villages he passed. This was guerrilla-held territory, and the locals stared at his car in astonishment . . . but only a few of the local militia decided to take potshots at him as he passed. Further on, the countryside began to get almost pleasant, and Michael realised what a beautiful country Havamala could be if only it could get its political problems sorted out.

The sun was setting when Michael finally approached the small town of Vista Grande, which was probably just as well, because in the hills beyond lay Melanie Black's private fortress. And there was no way he was going to drive up to *that* in broad daylight. Driving into the cover of a leafy copse, Michael told Kitt to wake him at eleven and settled down to get a few hours shut-eye. It had been a long hard day; and the night looked like being even harder.

No moon illuminated the sky when Michael finally prepared to set off again, and even the stars were going out as a bank of cloud rolled in from the west. That suited him very well, and he zipped up his black jacket tightly before reaching into the glove compartment and pulling out an automatic pistol. He hated using the things, but there were times when a man needed a little extra protection. And tonight was definitely one of those times.

With all its lights extinguished, Kitt drove up into the hills. When their destination finally came in sight, Michael pulled off to the edge of the road and began to scan the place with everything that Kitt could muster: scanners, x-rays, infra-red.

There were few lights, just in case the government's tiny airforce decided to launch a surprise night-strike. A complex of concrete buildings which had once been an exclusive and expensive boarding school lay surrounded by an electrified fence. There seemed to be only one main gate, but that came complete with guard-post and two armed men. Just finding his way inside was going to be a major problem.

He settled back to wait a bit longer, hoping that as many as possible of the people in the building would be asleep before he made his move. The guards at the gate were replaced at midnight, and he decided to give them another half hour to get bored and inattentive before he made his move.

Finally, Michael started the engine and turned Kitt off the road, using the

sensors to make his way in the dark as he crossed some rough country. He finally came to a halt by the perimeter fence, about two hundred yards from the main gate, and whispered some last instructions to Kitt.

The fence would doubtless be rigged with alarms, as well as being electrified, so there was no point trying to go through it. Instead Michael hit the ejector button, using just enough force to spring him over the top of the wire.

Landing silently in a crouch, Michael checked his gun and waited as Kitt drove off into the darkness. There was no sign of trouble.

Making his way through the shadows, Michael quietly approached the guard-post, keeping his eyes peeled for any signs of movement.

One of the men was outside the guard-post when Michael arrived, staring morosely at the moonless sky. Michael hit him on the side of the neck with a martial arts chop, and the man collapsed into his arms without a sound. He dragged him into the shadows, then returned to the doorway and started groaning softly.

"Hey, Pedro . . . what's the matter?" said the man within, but Michael just kept groaning until he emerged from the door. It was fists this time: one to the stomach, doubling the man up; then a second, upper-cut, to lay him out. He too was dragged away into the darkness, to join Pedro behind the hut.

A quick survey of the guard hut showed Michael where the cut-off switch was, and he turned off the electrification round the gate. A bunch of keys gave him the way to open up the padlocked gates themselves, and as he did so, he saw Kitt driving up toward him, right on schedule.

Closing the gates behind him, but not locking them, Michael got back into Kitt and drove slowly up toward the main buildings. When they were in scanner range, he stopped and surveyed the situation with Kitt's monitors.

It was easy enough for Kitt to provide him with floor-plans of the building; but the problems began when he used the infra-rays to pick up the heat from the bodies within. There were at least thirty people on the premises, and he had to find only one of them.

Integrating the infra-rays with the floor-plans, he found that at least twenty of those men were occupying a couple of large rooms on the ground floor. Michael guessed they'd once been classrooms, now turned into barracks; but why they weren't using the schools dormitories, he had no idea. He turned his attention to the upper of the building's two storeys.

Here, in a large room which he guessed *was* actually a dormitory, five people lay evenly spaced, as if in separate beds. Michael crossed them off his list too, and turned his attention to the smaller rooms; rooms which had probably once been the school's staff quarters.

These looked more promising. There were five people in three rooms; one

alone, the other two in pairs. He just hoped Melanie Black was the one who was on her own.

Driving round to the rear of the building, Michael used Kitt's microwave jammers to knock out any electronic alarms the place might contain and unlock the back-door. He talked through a few back-up plans with Kitt and left the car in Surveillance Mode before getting out; but from here on he was going to be pretty much on his own.

The back door gave access to the school kitchens, and Michael groped his way through them silently, using only a small electric torch. Once through them, however, he found himself in an electrically lit corridor. He would have preferred to make his approach in darkness, but he knew he couldn't hit the lights without attracting undue attention.

Turning the handle, he eased the door open and found the room was in darkness. Switching on his torch, he flicked it round the room . . . and saw a middle-aged man with a beard asleep in bed. Biting back an oath of disappointment, Michael closed the door again and moved on.

At the next room, Michael could hear the voices of two people talking; and one of them was a woman with a distinct American accent. Here was what he was looking for, but she was awake, accompanied, and probably armed. He paused for a moment, uncertainly. There was too much danger of discovery if he hung around waiting for the man to leave, so it looked like he'd have to go in. Now.

He tried to turn the door handle silently, but it clicked loudly, and the conversation within the room stopped instantly. There was nothing else to do but barge straight in, gun in hand.

Melanie Black was dressed in combat fatigues, sitting at a table talking to a swarthy hispanic, who was already reaching for his holster as Michael rushed in. But before the man could do anything, Michael dived full length, knocked him off his chair, and hit him over the head with his pistol. It wasn't pretty, it wasn't pleasant . . . but Michael's only concern was to knock the man out as soon as possible.

Expecting to be shot full of holes at any moment, Michael glanced up toward Melanie Black. But he was still between her and the door; and more importantly, between her and a submachine gun which lay on the bed. The girl stared at him for a few seconds as he got to his feet, and then decided what to do.

Melanie Black started screaming. Not screaming in panic or terror, but standing there and quite deliberately shrieking her head off. And, Michael realised as he sprang toward her, she had a *very* loud voice.

She struggled and fought as he got his arms round her, trying to slip past him and still making as much noise as she possibly could. Finally Michael got an arm round her neck, cutting off her screams with a sleeper hold. After a couple of seconds she went limp, and he hurriedly picked her up and threw her over his shoulder.

But the damage had been done now. Just as she'd intended, the girl's screams had woken everyone on the upper floor at least, if not every person in the entire building. As Michael came out into the corridor, a man with an automatic pistol appeared in the doorway of another room. Michael had no alternative but to let off a shot to keep the man pinned down . . . and that would certainly wake the people on the ground floor, if they weren't up and about already. Twenty of them. Michael didn't like to think about it.

He found the stairs again and dashed down, but the weight over his left shoulder was slowing him down. Another bullet bit into the plastered wall above his head, but while he had their leader, the bandits could only try to shoot to miss.

Reaching the lower corridor, Michael raced for the kitchen and wrenched open the door . . . only to find half a dozen armed men coming in through another entrance. Smiling, they raised their guns and took aim. Straight-faced, Michael raised his gun and pointed it at Melanie Black's head.

There were a few seconds of stand-off, neither side knowing quite what to do. Then Michael opened his mouth and yelled for Kitt as hard as he could. That puzzled his opponents, and they started glancing around for a second man.

Instead, a large black car suddenly smashed its way through the kitchen wall, scattering rubble in all directions and heading straight for the gunmen, stopping only just short of causing them injury. But as they panicked and flung themselves back, Michael raced forward, wrenching open Kitt's door and dumping the unconscious girl within.

"Reverse!" yelled Michael, even as he was swinging himself into the driver's seat. As he slammed the door shut, Kitt started doing just that; and Michael breathed a sigh of relief. At least he'd be relatively safe from small arms fire now.

Out in the darkness once more, Michael took over Kitt's controls and hurled the car round the corner of the building, heading for the gates as bullets whined through the air around them.

"Michael!" said Kitt suddenly. "Behind us! They've got some sort of rocket-launcher! And I'm not sure even *I* can stand up to *that*!"

"It's not something we want to find out about anyway, is it!" said Michael, suddenly hitting the turbo-boost.

As he did so, two long jets of flame roared out from the back of the car like flame-throwers. Michael had aimed them just right; he didn't actually want to kill the guys back there, but he did want the flame-trails to go just close enough to scatter them. And before they had time to recover from their panic, he hoped to be well clear of their rockets.

With the turbos in operation, the speedometer hit two hundred even before they reached the fence, and Kitt burst through the wire gates without a second thought. Then the black car was racing off into the safety of a very dark night.

Glancing over his shoulder, Michael saw that Melanie Black was still out like a light. What he'd do with her when she woke up he had no idea. His first concern was to get back through that war-zone again.

Slowing down when they'd covered a safe distance, Michael put Kitt back on automatic pilot and settled back to think.

What on earth was he going to tell the frontier guards *this* time?

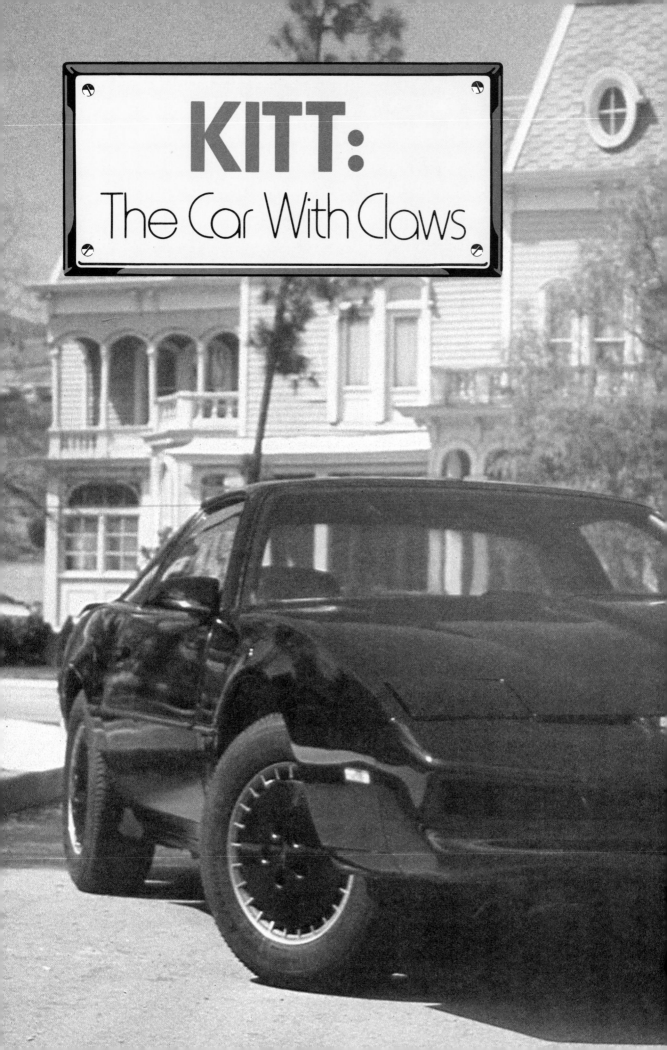

KITT:
The Car With Claws

A car that's more than a car . . . that's the *Knight Industries Two Thousand*, more often known as K.I.T.T., or simply 'Kitt'. Much more than simply being the car that gets Michael Knight from place to place, its assorted functions, both mechanical and computerised, enable it to deal with almost any crime-fighting situation; and the computer itself, having a personality of its own, is human enough to be thought of as a friend. Perhaps the closest friend Michael has, which is why Kitt is usually referred to as a 'he', rather than an 'it'.

Like many close friends, Michael and Kitt don't always get on. Kitt has evolved a very dry sense of humour, and he's obsessively interested in human emotions and feelings; although being still basically a machine, he doesn't always understand them. He tends to get annoyed at Michael's actions on occasion, and he tends to be rather over-protective; he's liable to object to any course of action in which he himself is likely to be damaged, or which might bring Michael to harm. The latter objection is just part of a wider feeling: Kitt is programmed never to take a human life, and preferably not to endanger it in any shape or form.

Kitt's real heart is his computerised 'robot brain', which is where his personality lies. His memory-banks already store an encyclopaedic general knowledge of almost everything under the sun, and he's learning more all the time. Being able to tap into the memories of other computers by telephone links helps the speed-learning process even more, and the result is that Kitt is something of a know-it-all. But though he does have a certain capacity for independent action on the spur of the moment, Kitt is still a machine, and most of his functions depend on his programming; either what has been placed in his circuits right from the start, or what is programmed into him specially by April Curtis. And a command from Michael still tends to over-ride any thoughts that Kitt might have on the matter.

Beyond the actual thinking 'brain' of the computer, Kitt also has a number of other functions. The car itself is of course an astounding piece of automotive technology, capable of enormous speeds; even more so over short distances with the aid of the *Turbo-Boost*, which gives Kitt the power to fly over or crash through things. Michael can also use the turbo-boosts as flame-throwers if the occasion arises. The car can also lay down oil-slicks, smokescreens, and so on, and is fitted with a number of other gadgets; ejector seats, grappling hooks, a vital-sign scanner, used to monitor blood pressure, heart rate, and the like, an internal oxygen supply, and micro-wave jammers, used to knock out security systems and telephone lines. Kitt is also self-repairing, and rarely has to go into one of F.L.A.G.'s garages for servicing.

Getting more technical, Kitt is fitted with a *Scanner*, the constantly rippling band of red-light on the front of the car, which can be used to x-ray anything within the locality. There

are also the *Infrarays*, used to track heat sources, such as another car's engines. Both these functions feed their information through to the *Dual Monitor Screens* on the dash-board inside the car. With all the flexibility of a TV video-player, these can provide instant replays, freeze-frames, close-ups and so on, as well as providing visual display for all the vast information in Kitt's memory banks; photographs, maps, or simply printed up data. But in answer to a specific question, Kitt is just as likely to tell Michael the answer vocally, rather than display it on the screen.

Finally, at the most advanced level, there are the *Automatic Pilot*, activated either by vocal command or by a button on the dashboard, which allows Kitt to drive by itself; *Pursuit Mode*, activated by button, which will put Kitt on the trail of any designated target with a tenacity that makes him impossible to shake off; and lastly, there is *Surveillance Mode*. This is not only a sensor field that registers any movement, person or vehicle within a hundred yard radius, but also, when activated, either by vocal command or by button, enables Kitt to take independent action, using most of the functions described already.

But Kitt's independence *is* limited. Basically, he still needs a human driver to fulfil all his potential, in the same way that Michael Knight needs a special car to fulfil his. Together they make a team, the front-line fighters in F.L.A.G.'s war against injustice. The *Knight Rider* team, bringing order to the chaotic wilderness of American crime .

CRIME-BUSTER KITT

THEN PUT YOUR FOOT DOWN, DOUGH-BRAIN... AND KEEP HEADING IN THE SAME DIRECTION...

MAYBE WE CAN PICK HIM UP.

"WHEN HE STOPS..."

MICHAEL! OVER HERE...

AH, HELLO DEVEN... APRIL...

WELL, WE DID IT, DEVEN...THE "THIN MAN'S" IN JAIL AND THE CASE IS CLOSED...

WHAT NEXT?

NEXT IS NOTHING... WE'VE GOT NOTHING ELSE ON THE BOOKS.

SO YOU MAY AS WELL TAKE A FEW DAYS OFF...

RELAX...DON'T GO LOOKING FOR TROUBLE.

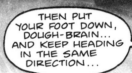

"UNTIL IT FINDS YOU AGAIN..."

THERE IT IS, BOSS! YOU WERE RIGHT!

Good Food!

'COURSE I WAS...I'M ALWAYS RIGHT!